CRAIG DAVID
BORN TO DO IT

Happy Christmas 2000, Love & Kisses Bubsey ?x—

WISE PUBLICATIONS
LONDON / NEW YORK / SYDNEY / PARIS / COPENHAGEN / MADRID / TOKYO

Exclusive distributors:
Music Sales Limited
8/9 Frith Street,
London W1D 3JB, England.
Music Sales Pty Limited
120 Rothschild Avenue, Rosebery,
NSW 2018, Australia.

Order No.AM968352
ISBN 0-7119-8626-6
This book © Copyright 2000 by Wise Publications.

Music arranged by Derek Jones.
Music processed by Paul Ewers Music Design.

Printed in the United Kingdom by
Printwise (Haverhill) Limited, Suffolk.

Your Guarantee of Quality:
As publishers, we strive to produce
every book to the highest commercial standards.
The music has been freshly engraved
and the book has been carefully designed to
minimise awkward page turns and to make
playing from it a real pleasure.
Particular care has been given to specifying
acid-free, neutral-sized paper made from pulps
which have not been elemental chlorine bleached.
This pulp is from farmed sustainable forests and
was produced with special regard for the environment.
Throughout, the printing and binding have been
planned to ensure a sturdy, attractive publication
which should give years of enjoyment.
If your copy fails to meet our high standards,
please inform us and we will gladly replace it.

Music Sales' complete catalogue describes
thousands of titles and is available in full colour
sections by subject, direct from Music Sales Limited.
Please state your areas of interest and send
a cheque/postal order for £1.50 for postage to:
Music Sales Limited, Newmarket Road,
Bury St. Edmunds, Suffolk IP33 3YB.

www.musicsales.com

Fill Me In

Words and Music by Craig David and Mark Hill

1. I was check-ing this girl next door when her par-ents went out. She'd phone say,
(Verse 2 see block lyric)

"Hey boy, come on right a - round."

So I knock on the door, you were stand-ing with a bot-tle of red wine rea-dy to pour.

Dressed in long, black sat - in, lace to the floor.

To Coda ⊕

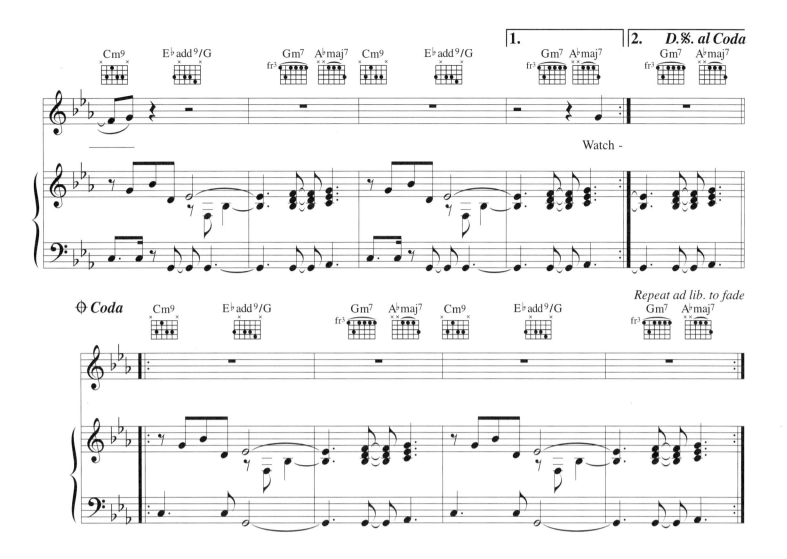

Watch-

Repeat ad lib. to fade

Verse 2:
Whenever the coast was clear and she'd ask me to come out
I'd say "Hey girl, come on right around"
So she knocked at the door
I was standing with the keys in my hand to the four-by-four
Jumped in my ride checking that nobody saw
The club we went in, we got down
Bounce, bounce to the rhythm
Saw it was early morning
Thought we'd better be leaving
So I gave you my jacket for you to hold
Told you to wear it cos you felt cold
I mean me and her didn't mean to break the rules
I wasn't trying to play your mum and dad for fools
We were just doing things young people in love do
Parents trying to find out what we were up to.

Saying why can't you keep your promises no more
Saying you'll be home by twelve, come strolling in at four
Out with your girls, but leaving with the boy next door
Can you fill me in? (fill me in)
Wearing a jacket who's property
Said you'd been queuing for a taxi
But you left all your money on the TV (you tell 'em, babe)
Can you fill me in? (can you fill me in).

Can't Be Messing 'Round

Words and Music by Craig David

I must ad-mit that she was get-tin' to me,— wait-in' for me. Want-ing me to hold her oh, so tight.

To-geth-er, for-ev-er, wher-ev-er, what-ev-er. She said she could-n't find no-bo-dy bet-ter.

Was-n't gon-na give up on me nev-er. She said Ooh———— you're look-in' so fly————

———— ev-'ry time you pass me by. I like the— way—— you move your bo — dy.—

Girl, I must ad-mit— you're look-in' real fit, let's chill for a lit-tle bit. I know you wan-na get with me.— But

girl you know— I'm not free.————————— One two three four— five six sev-en eight nine ten.

———— Come on let me hit it a-gain, come on let me sing it a-gain. Won't pre-

- tend, can't be mess-ing 'round with my girl-friend. One two three four— five six sev-en eight nine ten.

Come on let me hit it a-gain, come on let me sing it a-gain. Won't pre-

1.
-tend, can't be mess-ing 'round with my girl-friend.

2.
-tend, can't be mess-ing 'round with my girl-friend.
Rap: Girl -

friend, this love we got__ be gold-en and you know you got__ me op-en.
(For repeat see block text)

1° R.H. tacet

Since the day we start-ed talk-ing you and I've had this spe-cial lit-tle some-thing.

One two three four— five six sev-en eight nine ten.— Come on let me hit it a-gain,

come on let me sing it a-gain. Won't pre-tend, can't be mess-ing 'round with my girl-friend.

One two three four— five six sev-en eight nine ten.— Come on let me hit it a-gain,

come on let me sing it a-gain. Won't pre-tend, can't be mess-ing 'round with my girl-friend.

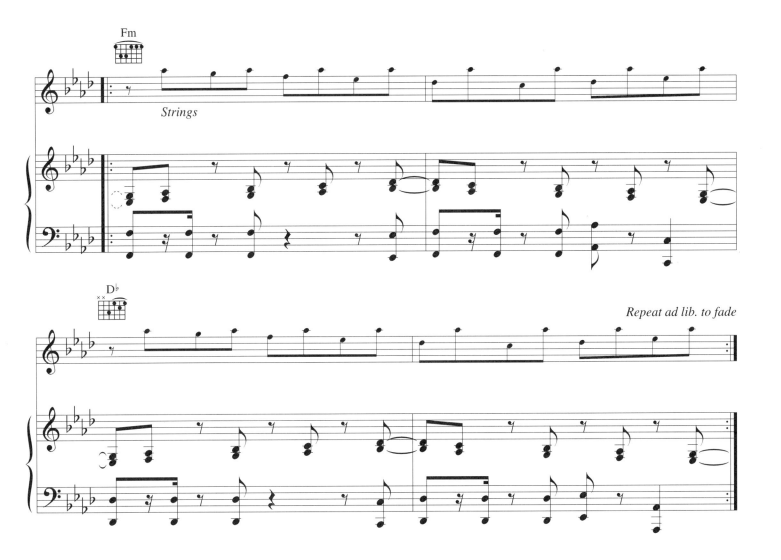

Verse 2:

It seems like every day girl you wanna be calling me
And when I step outside you always follow me
You said that you were really feeling Sisqo's song
About that thong, th, thong, thong, thong did I wanna see?
And when you talk like that you know you're really tempting me
But I got a girl at home who'll do the same for me
And that's the way that it's gotta be, gotta be, so listen now lady.

Ooh, I like your profile, the way you talk and your smile
But you gotta understand lady, I'm not cheating on my baby
Ooh, you know this ain't right, I'm going home to my girl tonight
And I'm sorry that we couldn't get it on
But the love for my girl's too strong.

1, 2, 3, 4, 5, 6, 7, 8, 9, 10, come on *etc.*

Rap Repeat:

With who me? The one and only C-R-A-I-G, come on
Now let me deliver this properly (yeah, yeah)
So the world can see that I, ain't the type of guy
And why should I, make my girlfriend cry?
Can't deny the girl I met was real fly
But it's just you that puts me on a natural high
So I just walked on by (ha, ha), saying my oh my (yeah)
I ain't gon' let no other girl start troublin'
Lose someone like you, you must be joking.

Rendezvous

Words and Music by Craig David and Mark Hill

Craig Dav-id this is how we do. Yeah, well c'm-on, check it out.

(What-cha do-ing cos we'll be ren-dez-vous-ing and you know we'll be get-ting some, get-ting jig-gy just for fun.

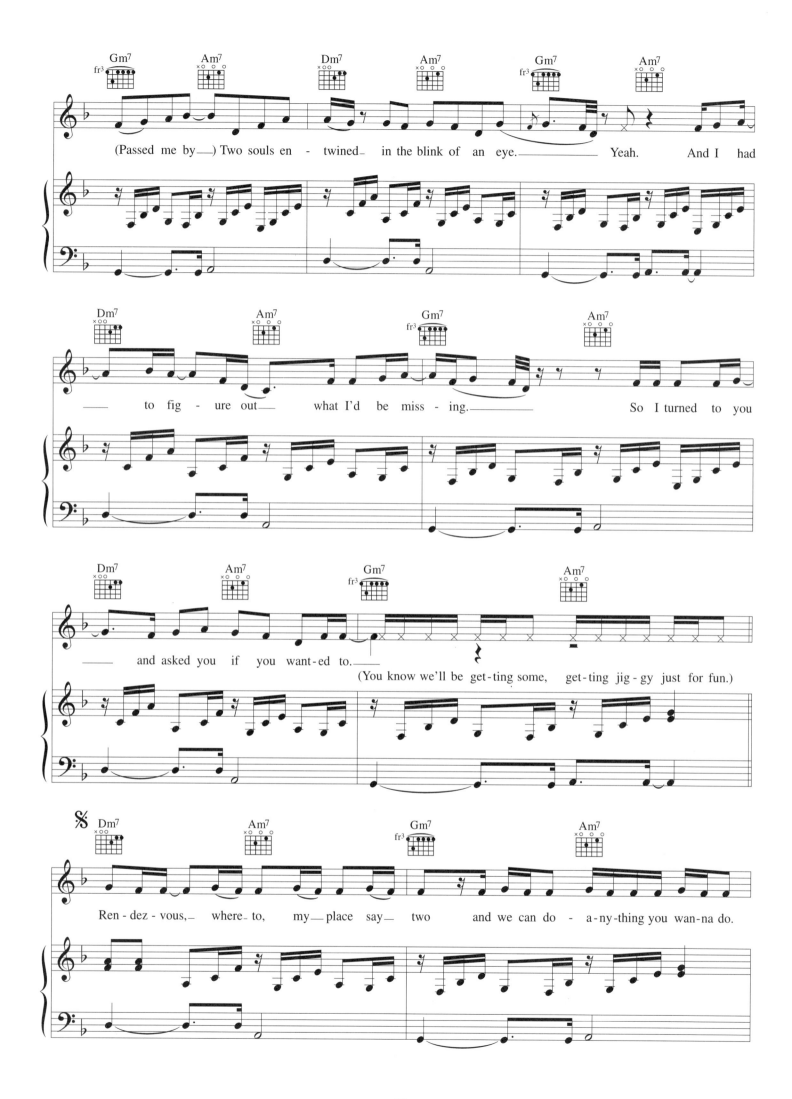

Verse 2:
I'm just sitting here daydreaming about you and all the things you do
Girl feels so right
And all I know is you're the one for me, that special kinda' lady
In my life, in my life.

Well here I am writing you a love song
Holding back those years, it's been so long
And I can't deny the way that I'm feeling (feeling)
It's true, so girl that's why I'm asking you, can we…

Rendezvous *etc.*

7 Days

Words and Music by Craig David, Mark Hill and Darren Hill

Yeah, Craig David, Seven Days, check it out, yeah."

1. On my way___ to see___ my friends___ who lived a cou-ple of blocks a-way from me. (Ow)___
(Verse 2 see block lyric)

___ As I walked___ through the sub - way,___ must-'ve been a-bout quar-ter past

three, in front of me___ stood a beau-ti-ful___ ho-ney with a beau-ti-ful bo - dy.___

24

Wed-nesday and on— Thurs - day and Fri - day and Sa-tur- day, we chilled on Sun - day.

Repeat ad lib. to fade

Verse 2:
Nine was the time cos I'll be getting mine
And she was looking fine
Smooth talker, she told me
She'd love to unfold me all night long
Ooh, I loved the way she kicked it
From the front to the back she flipped it
(Back she flipped it, ooh, the way she kicked it)
And I, oh-oh, I, yeah
Hope that she'd care
Cos I'm a man who'll always be there
Ooh, yeah
I'm not a man to play around, baby
Ooh, yeah
Cos a one-night stand isn't really fair
From the first impression, girl, hmm
You don't seem to be like that
Cos there's no need to chat
For there'll be plenty of time for that
From the subway to my home
Endless ringing on my phone
When you're feeling all alone
All you gotta do is just call me, call me.

Monday took her for a drink *etc.*

29

Follow Me

Words and Music by Craig David and Mark Hill

miss-ing my lov-ing,_____ ask-ing am I gon-na give it to ya.

She said___ I like the way___ you put___ it down___ on___ me,___

___ me,___ me,___ ba-by,___ that there's no-thing more___ she'd rath-

-er do,_____ do_____ than

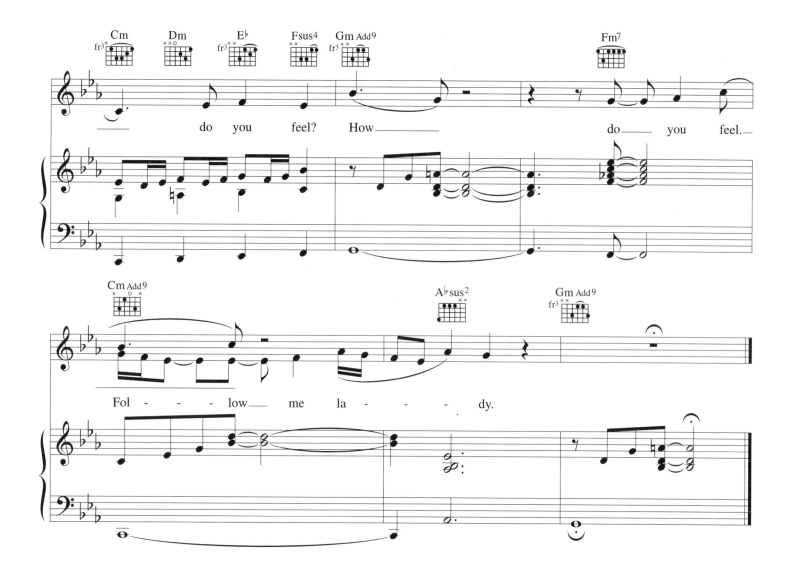

Verse 2:
Relax, unwind and just take your time, take, take your, take your time
I would like to show you, get to know you, hold you, kiss you
Running my fingers through your hair
How do you like it?
Let's just take it nice and slow and enjoy the flow.

Chorus 2:
Follow me (alright), follow me to my bedroom
(You know what you gotta do, you know what you gotta do take my hand)
Follow me, follow me to my bedroom
(This'll be a night you won't forget)
Follow me, follow me to my bedroom
(Follow me, follow me darling)
Follow me, follow me to my bedroom
Can you follow me?

Chorus 3:
How do you feel? (Both our bodies)
How do you feel? (This'll be a night you won't forget)
How do you feel? (All I wanna know)
How do you feel?

Last Night

Words and Music by Craig David and Mark Hill

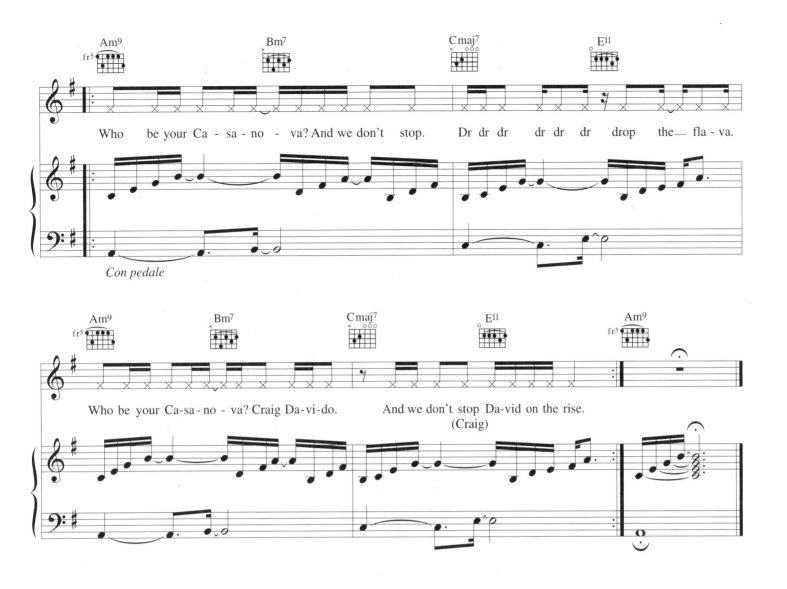

Verse 2:

Girl you had me trippin' (girl you've got me trippin')
My heart was feenin' from the beginning (from the beginning)
Just to hold your body drove me crazy (girl you drove me crazy)
And it weren't like I had to pretend that I'll be a casanova
If you'd only let me show ya
Felt like a drink, so we went to the bar
Next thing we found ourselves in the back of my car
Making her laugh and giggle, ha ha
My body all over your (ha ha)
I didn't want to take it too far, especially in the car
Got more respect for ya (signorita) ooh yeah
Now you're my partner a come on.

Yere sera *etc.*

Time To Party

Words and Music by Craig David, Mark Hill and Jimmy Seals

Am⁷   Bm⁷

On Fri - day,___ time to par - ty.___ Let me see you

Em¹¹

swing and_ sway.___ Tell me are you with me, are you with_ me?___

Am⁷   Bm⁷

1. Fri - day,___ pay day,___ rea - dy to do_ the things_ we love.
(Verse 2 see block lyric)

Em¹¹   Am⁷

___ We're gon-na get_ our groove on all night long.___ (Ho___ hey!

Give it up now for the D. J. (Uh-huh, yeah.) and put your hands where my eyes can see. It may be rain-ing but who cares a-bout the wea-ther? (Get up) Cos when the heat is on we'll all be get-ting wet-ter. (Stand up) It's the start of the week-end,

Verse 2:
Everybody's feeling right (feeling right)
Cos we know it's party night (ooh yeah)
All the ladies looking tight
Whether silk or satin, lace or leather
Ooh what a sight
Here's where the party starts things can only get better (get up)
Just make your way on to the dance floor get together (stand up)
It's the start of the weekend don't waste no time
For tonight is your night.

On Friday *etc.*

Walking Away

Words and Music by Craig David and Mark Hill

Well, I saw them with my own eyes spreading those lies. And, well I don't wanna live my life, too many sleepless nights. Not mentioning the fights. I'm sorry to say lady... I'm walking away from the troubles in my life. I'm walking away,

Verse 2:

Well I'm, so tired baby

Things you say, you're driving me away

Whispers in the powder room baby, don't listen to the games they play

Girl I thought you'd realise, I'm not like them other guys

Cos I say them with my own eyes, you should've been more wise, and

Well I don't wanna live my life, too many sleepless nights

Not mentioning the fights, I'm sorry to say lady.

I'm walking away *etc.*

Once In A Lifetime

Words and Music by Craig David and Mark Hill

Once in a life - time I have the chance to find— the key—
to my dreams._ that it's so good for me.
(And I— know)

Once in a life - time I have the chance to find— the key—
to my dreams._ that it's so good for me.
(And I— know)

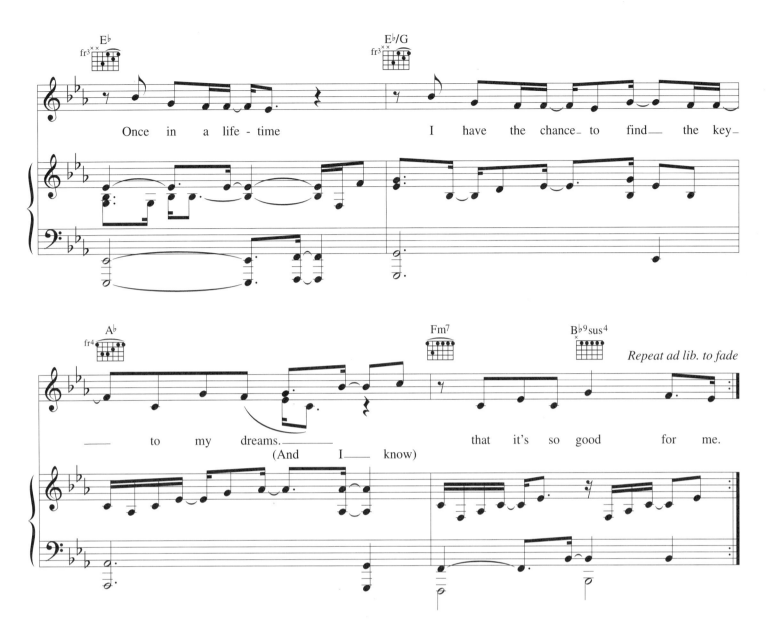

Verse 2:
I was lost couldn't find my way
You took my hand and chased my blues away
Your inspiration is guiding me through
I'm feeling brand new
Memories of days gone by
Hurting always hurting
You've taken my pain away finally
You set me free babe.

Once in a lifetime *etc.*

Booty Man

Words and Music by Craig David and Mark Hill

Verse 2:
One, two unbuckle my shoe kissing and cuddling at my crib after the venue and I
Didn't wanna take it too fast so I said slow, slow I gotta make some calls so keep it down low
She was like I can't believe you wanna talk instead of making love to me
Five minutes chilling next thing it's my name she's calling.

If you're looking *etc.*

You Know What

Words and Music by Craig David and Mark Hill

71

Verse 2:
Now I can't seem to get over you appearing in everything that I do
It was only last week Friday when I saw you out with your girlfriends walking
'Round my way (wanted to stop) yeah-e yeah
I feel when all's said and done
From this love I've had I've learnt a lot yeah
I never thought you'd leave me no
But you know what (hey, hey, hey)

We were meant to be *etc.*

Rewind

Words and Music by Craig David and Mark Hill

you know the Art-ful Dod-ger do it like that.____ With Craig Dav-id all ov-er your...

D. J. it's all up to you.____ When the crowd__ go wild____

tell me what - cha gon' do?____

Re - e - e - wind. When the crowd say bo se-lec - ta. Re-e-e - e-e-e-wind when the